It's another Quality Book from CGP

This book is for anyone doing GCSE Food Technology.

It contains lots of tricky questions designed
to make you sweat — because that's the only
way you'll get any better.

It's also got the odd daft bit in to try and make
the whole thing at least vaguely entertaining for you.

What CGP is all about

Our sole aim here at CGP is to produce the highest quality
books — carefully written, immaculately presented and
dangerously close to being funny.

Then we work our socks off to get them out to you
— at the cheapest possible prices.

Contents

SECTION FOUR — MARKETING AND INDUSTRY

SECTION FIVE — DESIGN AND DEVELOPMENT

Published by Coordination Group Publications Ltd.

Contributors:
Victoria Brereton
Sally Lister
Andy Park
Alan Rix
Elaine Rooney
Jane Scott
Rachel Selway
Alice Shepperson
Claire Thompson
Judith-Ann Wardlaw
Chrissy Williams

With thanks to Susan Hosking, Tim Major and Glenn Rogers for the proofreading.

ISBN: 1-84146-799-5

Groovy website: www.cgpbooks.co.uk

Jolly bits of clipart from CorelDRAW

With thanks to TECHSOFT UK Ltd. for permission to use
a screenshot from 'DESIGN TOOLS — 2D DESIGN'

Printed by Elanders Hindson, Newcastle upon Tyne

Design Brief

Q1 Explain briefly why companies carry out consumer research.

Q2 What is the purpose of a design brief and what should it include?

Q3 Each of the people or groups of people below have
a problem. Write one or two sentences for each
one, describing a product that meets their need.

1. Mr Alfonso is the owner of a restaurant that specialises in beef. Customers
   who buy the sirloin steak always compliment him on the tenderness of the
   beef, but many people say the dish isn't interesting enough.

2. Mr and Mrs Jones' seven-year-old daughter only likes brightly-coloured
   sweets, but she is allergic to the artificial colourings used in most products.

3. Susan has recently discovered that she is lactose intolerant, but her favourite
   food is cheesecake.

Q4 Companies need to be aware of the existing market and existing products when
they think about designing and manufacturing a new product. Give three reasons
why companies might decide to introduce a new product into the market.

Q5 Explain the following terms in relation to the design process in Food Technology.

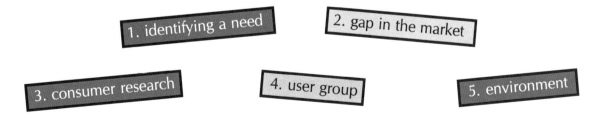

1. identifying a need

2. gap in the market

3. consumer research

4. user group

5. environment

Design briefs — PVC Y-fronts with tassels... mmm...
Knowing the design process is half the battle with D&T. Make sure you know every stage of the
process, what it's for, and what order the stages come in. After that, it should be a breeze...

Research

Q1   Research is used to gather ideas before you start designing your product.
      Describe three things that you could aim to find out from your research.

Q2   There are two forms of research — primary and secondary. Primary
      research is when you collect information yourself and secondary research
      is when you use information collected by someone else. Say whether
      each of the sources of information below is primary or secondary.

          a) Internet   c)   interviews   e)   magazines

          b) letters   d)   books   f)   newspapers

Q3   The table below shows three different ways of carrying out primary research.
      Copy and complete the table using the sentences from the box below.

Method of Research	Use
Questionnaires	
Disassembling and tasting existing products	
Weighing and measuring an existing product	

a)   Tells you how a current product is made and how it is put
     together. It will help you to decide which ingredients and
     processes you need to use and how your product will
     meet consumers' needs.

b)   Gives you an idea of the weight, size and shape of your
     product and its sensory features.

c)   Tells you about people's likes and dislikes. This will help
     you identify market trends and your target group.

Sensory analysis — finding out
how a product tastes, feels,
looks and smells

Q4   Once you have completed your research, you need to decide how to use the information
      you have gathered. What is the proper term for this stage of the design process?

Design Specification

Q1   Write a sentence to explain what a design specification is.

Q2   Think of as many factors as you can that could be included in a
design specification. Draw a spider diagram to show your ideas.

Q3   Below is a list of specification points for different products.
Write out the appropriate specification points next to the products.

vegan chocolate	must be suitable for eating on the way to work
fruit-flavoured cordial	must contain no dairy products
a milkshake for slimmers	should taste of real oranges
a cereal bar	to contain less than 1% fat

Q4   Write three points that could be included in
the design specification for a Christmas cake.

Design Specification

1.

2.

3.

Generating Proposals

Q1 Give a brief description of each of the following terms, and say how they might help you to generate ideas for a design proposal.

 a) mood board

 b) brainstorming

 c) an existing product

Q2 Designers often use sketches to present their ideas when they're generating proposals.

a) Explain briefly why sketches are used for design proposals.

b) What is the proper term for labelling and adding notes to those sketches?

Q3 Your notes should cover the size and shape of your design. Write down five other things that you could include in your notes in order to explain your ideas.

Q4 Copy and complete the table below by choosing three different ways of presenting your designs, and giving a brief description of each.

Presentation technique	Description

Marry me, my darling.

Development

Q1   The development stage of the design process involves exploring the chosen design in detail. Give three features of a design that you could consider during the development stage of the design process.

Q2   It is helpful to try actually making your product when you're developing your design. Give the proper name for a design 'model' and write a sentence to explain why this is such a useful part of the design process.

Q3   Name three ways you could record how you have developed a design.

Q4   Use the words in the box below to complete the following sentences.

Once you have developed your designs using models or .... , you need

to .... the results. This will allow you to make .... to your design

and improve the product, or make it ready for .... It is also important

that the design is checked to ensure that it meets the ....

design specification	mass production	
modifications	analyse	taste tests

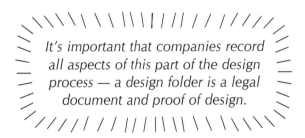

It's important that companies record all aspects of this part of the design process — a design folder is a legal document and proof of design.

'Developing' is an anagram of 'Deep Loving' — how nice...

This part of the design process is usually the trickiest for people to get their heads round. Think about what developing a design means, and show your thoughts in a spider diagram — it'll come in handy in the exam.

Research

Q1   Which of the following are ways of testing a product?

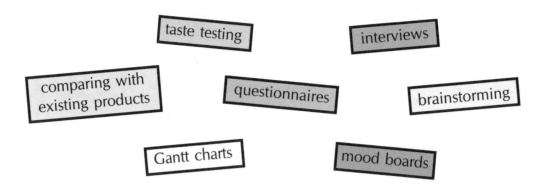

taste testing

interviews

comparing with existing products

questionnaires

brainstorming

Gantt charts

mood boards

Q2   Imagine you have carried out a survey for people to test the product you have designed. Write five standard questions that could appear in that survey.

Q3   Should evaluations be carried out at the beginning, the end or throughout the whole process? Explain your answer.

Have you ever considered buying low-cholesterol spread instead of your usual margarine?

Q4   Copy and complete the passage below using words from the box.

By the time you've arrived at a final ...., you should have worked out the best .... and tools to use. You should also have worked out how much .... and money the .... of each item is going to require. It is also very important to plan the ....
thoroughly. A .... is probably the best way of presenting this information, and looks very impressive too.

time	flow chart	materials
assembly process	production	design

Manufacturer's Specification

Q1   What is a manufacturer's specification?

Q2   Manufacturers' specifications are sometimes presented using working drawings.
Explain what is meant by working drawings.

Q3   Name one way of presenting a costing sheet on a PC.

Q4   Below is a list of points that should be included in a manufacturer's specification.
Copy and complete the sentences below using the words from the box.

> tolerances   construction   sizes and weights   finishing
>
> costs   costings   quality control

1. Clear .... details — explaining exactly how each part is going to be made and
   how the product will be assembled.

2. .... — precise measurements of each part.

3. .... — the boundaries that the product must fall within. This can apply to
   weight, colour, taste, size, etc.

4. .... details — any special sequencing for finishing.

5. .... instructions — where and how the manufacturing process should be checked.

6. .... — how much each ingredient costs, and details of other .... involved.

Planning Production

Q1   Explain how charts might help you to plan the production process.

Q2   Describe what a Gantt chart is used for and how it works.

Q3   The graphical symbols below are used in flow charts. Use the
      words on the right to say what stage of a flow chart they represent.

Process

Decision

Start/end

Q4   Describe what a summative evaluation is and what it involves.

Q5   Below are seven stages on how to tackle an exam. Draw a flow chart, putting
      the stages in the right order. Use the correct graphical symbols for each stage.

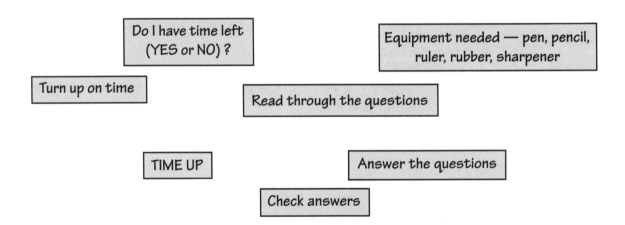

Do I have time left
(YES or NO) ?

Equipment needed — pen, pencil,
ruler, rubber, sharpener

Turn up on time

Read through the questions

TIME UP

Answer the questions

Check answers

You can make flow charts for virtually anything...

...like making a cup of tea, for instance. You could even draw some accompanying designs, and annotate
them. And while you're drinking your tea, you might like to think about how you're going to hide your
designs and what you're going to say if someone asks you what you've been doing for the last two hours.

Carbohydrates — Sugar

Q1 Carbohydrates are split into three groups. What is each group called?

Q2 Copy and complete this passage, filling in the blanks with words from the box.

fructose	starch	polysaccharides	digest	energy	stores

> Carbohydrates are needed in the body to provide us with .... If we eat
> too many carbohydrates, the body .... them as fat. Glucose and
> .... are examples of simple sugars — these are easier to .... than
> starches because they are made of smaller molecules, and are easier for the
> body to break down. Non- .... can't be digested by the
> body but they are essential to the diet to prevent constipation.

Q3 Copy and complete the following sentence by selecting **a**, **b**, **c** or **d** from the list below:

Sugar is needed in cake making...

a)   ...to flatten the cake.

b)   ...to ferment the cake mixture.

c)   ...to add fibre.

d)   ...to add texture and volume.

No, there are no known problems with high-fibre diets.

Q4 Sugar is called lots of different things on ingredients labels.
Write down three of these alternative names.

Q5 Give three reasons why a sugar substitute may be better than sugar.

Is that an "NSP over-ingestion" side effect — or a breeze?...
Sugar isn't only used to sweeten things. In jam it acts as a preservative, helps with setting and adds texture and volume. It also helps to stop cakes, biscuits and pastries drying out. And it can add colour too.

Carbohydrates — Starch

Q1   Name the three main uses of starch for making food products.

Q2   The following statements show an example of gelatinisation, but they're
        in the wrong order. Rewrite them so they're in the right order.

The milk is absorbed into the cornflour gradually.

The milk is heated gradually.

Cornflour and milk are combined to make a smooth paste.

The milk and cornflour can now be called a gel.

When the temperature reaches 80 °C the cornflour
particles break open and thicken the mixture.

Q3   Copy and complete the following sentence by selecting **a**, **b**, or **c**.

Modified starches are known as...

a)   ...smart starches.

b)   ...thickening starches.

c)   ...viscous starches.

Q4   Write a couple of sentences to explain what "syneresis" is
        and how modified starches can be useful for dealing with it.

Q5   The table below shows three different ways modified starch is used in manufacturing.
        Copy and complete it by giving an example of a food for each one.

Use	Example
To thicken	
To prevent syneresis	
To thicken low-calorie emulsions	

Carbohydrates — Cereals and Flour

Q1   Which of these flours is used in the production of bread?

   a)   soft

   b)   strong

   c)   very very long

   d)   self-raising

   e)   plain

Q2   Match each of the products below to the correct type of flour.

   a)   Strong wheat   c)   Durum wheat   e)   Maize

   b)   Oatmeal   d)   Rye   f)   Soft wheat

Progress

rye bread   oat cakes   shortbread

corn muffins   pasta   popcorn

Victoria sandwich porridge   white bread

Q3   The flour used in baking bread has a protein called gluten in it.
      Write a couple of sentences to explain what happens to make gluten become
      stretchy and elastic, and what this does to the bread during making and baking.

Q4   Copy and complete the two sentences below.

   a)   A (high / low) gluten flour is needed to make light-textured cake.

   b)   A (high / low) gluten flour is needed to make light-textured bread.

Q5   Write a sentence to explain why wheatgerm causes bread to have a denser texture.

To do well at Food Tech you need to be a gluten for punishment...

Soft flour and strong flour come from different parts of the world. Soft flour is made from wheat grown in
places with long summers and short winters (like Mediterranean countries). Strong flour, on the other hand,
comes from wheat grown in places like Canada — it needs hot summers and very cold winters.

Carbohydrates — Wheat

Q1 Copy and complete the table below using the phrases from the box to show how flour is made.

Process	Action
Cleaning	
Conditioning	
Milling	
Further milling	
Mixing	
Sterilising	

> Different flavours are mixed to vary textures and flavours.
> Grains are passed through rollers and the endosperm is scraped away.
> Sieved and rubbed clean.
> Passed through rollers again.
> Ensures the flour is safe to eat.
> Dried or moistened.

Q2 In your own words, describe briefly how each of the following are milled:

a) White flour

b) Wholemeal flour

c) Stoneground flour

Q3 Which of the following provides vitamins and minerals in the wheat grain?

a) The endosperm

b) The bran

c) The wheatgerm

Q4 Copy the diagram of a wheat grain and complete it by labelling it correctly.

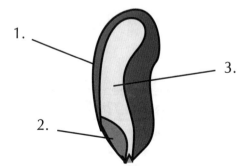

Proteins

Q1   There are two basic reasons why our bodies need protein. What are they?

Q2   In your own words, describe the difference between high and low biological value proteins.

Q3   Copy and complete the table with the correct sources of proteins from the box below.

High biological value proteins	Low biological value proteins

nuts	meat	eggs	pulses
fish	cereals	soya beans	milk

Q4   Copy and complete the passage below using words from the box.

Protein is important to help .... new cells and also to .... old and damaged cells.

The proteins we eat include meat, ... and poultry. The eggs, milk and other dairy produce

we get from .... are also high in protein.

High-protein foods can be .... when they are undercooked or stored at the wrong

temperature. This is because they are perfect places for .... to grow.

fish	dangerous	bacteria	grow	repair	animals

Proteins — Fish and Alternatives

Q1 Fish is high in protein but it also provides other essential nutrients. What are they?

Q2 Copy and complete the table below by giving an example of each type of fish and a dish it can be used to make.

Fish	Example	Dish
Oily fish		
Shellfish		
White fish		

Q3 Which two alternative proteins are made using soya beans?

Q4 What are the two main ingredients of Quorn?

Q5 Give two examples of types of food that each of the following meat alternatives can be made into.

　a)　Tofu　　　　　　b)　TVP　　　　　　c)　Quorn

Q6 Say whether each of the following statements is true or false.

　a)　Meat alternatives are high in flavour.

　b)　Meat alternatives are low in protein.

　c)　Meat alternatives are unsuitable for vegetarians.

　d)　Some meat alternatives are suitable for use in desserts.

There's something fishy here — where's the Quorny gag...

Some meat replacements are a bit drab and tasteless. But these are often made a bit nicer by soaking them in a marinade (a mixture of flavoursome stuff like herbs, oil, vinegar and wines) before cooking.

Vitamins and Minerals

Q1   Listed below are some vitamins. For each one, give
its common name, or the vitamin group it is found in.

a)   Calciferol

b)   Ascorbic acid

c)   Folic acid

d)   Niacin

Q2   Copy and complete the table below with the correct information.
One line has already been filled in for you.

Vitamin	Function	Source
A		
B Group		
C	Protects against infection, helps absorb iron and calcium, maintains cell walls, heals wounds.	Citrus fruit, green vegetables, peppers and potatoes
D		

Q3   Copy out the following sentence and complete it using either **a**, **b**, **c**, or **d**.

Calcium is necessary in the diet...

a)   ...to release energy from food.

b)   ...to form red blood cells.

c)   ...to form and maintain strong bones and teeth.

d)   ...to heal cuts and wounds.

Q4   Name three good sources of iron in the diet.

Q5   Write down four reasons why we should include
a good amount of fruit and vegetables in our diet.

Fruit and Vegetables

Q1 Shania is seventeen and very conscious of her image. She is concerned that if she doesn't eat the right foods, her health will suffer and she might get spots or put on weight.

In a typical day Shania eats:

> Breakfast: one slice of toast with jam, a glass of orange juice.
> Lunch: meatballs with rice, can of coke, lemon meringue pie.
> Evening meal: chips, peas, fish, cup of tea, sweets.
> Snacks: chocolate bar, apple, can of lemonade.

a) How many portions of fruit or vegetables has Shania eaten?

b) How many portions of fruit or vegetables should she be eating?

c) Write out an alternative meal plan, including the right amount of fruit and vegetables.

Q2 Say whether each of the following statements is true or false.

a) Vegetables should be cooked in a lot of water.

b) There is more vitamin C in a raw carrot than a cooked carrot.

c) Vegetables should be stored in light airy places.

d) Fruit and vegetables should be chopped into large pieces to save vitamin content.

e) Unpeeled or thinly peeled fruit and vegetables have a higher vitamin content than completely peeled ones.

I've got a lovely bunch of coconuts.

Q3 Say which two ways of cooking are the most suitable for fruit and vegetables and explain why.

Q4 Other than vitamins and minerals, what other qualities do fruit and vegetables bring to a meal? Give at least three qualities and an example for each.

Q5 There are eight types / varieties of vegetable in total. Three of these are tubers (e.g. potatoes), leaves (e.g. cabbage) and roots (e.g. carrots). Name the other five types of vegetable and give an example for each one.

Fats and Oils

Q1   Copy and complete this table to show the six main types of fats
and oils, and whether they are of animal or vegetable origin.

Animal fats	Vegetable fats

Q2   Copy and complete this paragraph, filling in the blanks with words from the box below.

Fats are very useful for lots of reasons in food .... We can use them to give texture

(e.g. .... crumbly pastries), or holding .... (e.g. working with sugar to make

foams for light and fluffy cakes). Fats make food .... better (e.g. pastry or shortbread),

and they add .... too (e.g. golden fairy cakes). Fats are useful for keeping foods

.... and for creating a waterproof barrier, e.g. spreads on sandwiches.

shortened	taste	colour
moist	air	manufacture

Q3   What are the three nutritional benefits that our bodies get from fat?

Q4   Cholesterol forms part of all of our cell membranes, but why do
scientists think that too much cholesterol in the diet can be bad?

Q5   Which type of fat contains more cholesterol — animal fat or vegetable fat?

Q6   Name four different types of vegetable oil.

No

Dairy Products

Q1 Milk is a baby's first food for a reason. Why do you think milk is so good for babies and young children?

Q2 Copy and complete the table below with the correct information.

Type of milk	Fat content	Flavour
	3.5%	Creamy
Skimmed		Light
	1.75%	

Q3 Copy and complete the following sentence by choosing **a**, **b**, **c**, or **d** as the right ending.

Homogenised milk is milk that...

a) ...has had the fat removed.

b) ...has had half of the fat removed.

c) ...has the fat distributed throughout the milk.

d) ...has a longer shelf-life.

Q4 What process is milk put through to kill harmful bacteria and make it last longer?

Q5 Which type of milk lasts the longest?

Q6 Briefly explain how each of these types of milk have been treated:

a) Homogenised

b) Pasteurised

c) Ultra Heat Treated (UHT)

Q7 List three things that cream can be processed into.

Q8 Explain how cheese is made.

Eggs

Q1 What's the right term for when an egg becomes
semi-solid in cooking (e.g. like when it sets in a quiche)?

Q2 What are the three main minerals found in eggs?

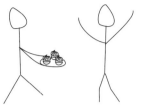

Q3 Say whether each of the following statements is true or false.

a) The whole of an egg coagulates at 60 °C.

b) Lecithin is the natural emulsifier found in eggs.

c) Eggs contain Vitamin F.

d) The protein in eggs stretches to hold air when it's beaten.

Q4 Why is it especially important that eggs are cooked thoroughly
for pregnant women, the elderly, and young babies?

Eggs are so versatile.

Q5 Below is a list of things that eggs can be used for in cooking.
For each one, give an example of a food or dish it would be useful for.

a) binding

b) thickening

c) garnishing

d) glazing

e) coating

f) coagulating

g) emulsifying

h) trapping air

I brushed two lots of egg coating onto this pastry — it's double glazed...
This eggs-citing page is eggs-actly what you need to get an eggs-cellent result in your eggs-am.
So learn all this stuff and you should eggs-cell. Ho-ho, it's an egg pun eggs-travaganza.

Combining Ingredients

Q1   Write a brief definition of each of the words below.

Q2   Explain the role of an emulsifier and give an example.

Q3   Say whether each of the following definitions is true or false.

a) Lecithin is the emulsifier contained in egg yolk.

b) Starchy suspensions can be prevented from separating by chilling.

c) Pectin helps jam set when mixed with fruit acid and sugar.

d) Sugar helps to stabilise a foam to stop it changing shape.

Q4   Give an example of each of the following types of
mixture — emulsion, suspension, gel and foam.

Oh, the joys of gel...

Q5   Say which of the following statements are true and which are false.

a) Hot chocolate is a homogenous solution.

b) In a suspension the solids always float about in the liquid.

c) Sugar can stop a foam separating.

d) You could call gel a thick solution.

Q6   A food manufacturer can't seem to stop their new salad dressing from separating.
They suggest that the consumer shakes the bottle before use. What could the
manufacturers add to the actual dressing to prevent it from separating?

Foam — eating it makes you soft in the head...

Solutions and suspensions... urg. The big difference between them is that in a suspension the
ingredients keep their own properties — they don't change, they just mix. But in a solution the
ingredients merge to create a new, homogenous liquid. Easy. So don't forget it. Ever.

Different Types of Production

Q1   Describe what a prototype is used for. At what stage
of the manufacturing process is a prototype made?

Q2   Write a short description of each of the following processes.

a) jobbing production

b) batch production

c) continuous production

Q3   Copy and complete this table to show an advantage and a
disadvantage of each of the three production methods <u>for a company</u>.

Jobbing	Advantage	
	Disadvantage	
Batch	Advantage	
	Disadvantage	
Continuous	Advantage	
	Disadvantage	

Q4   Do the same for the table below, which shows advantages and
disadvantages of the different methods <u>for consumers</u>.

Jobbing	Advantage	
	Disadvantage	
Batch	Advantage	
	Disadvantage	
Continuous	Advantage	
	Disadvantage	

Q5   For each of the following products, say which of the three methods
mentioned above you think should be used. Explain your answer.

Different Types of Production

Q1 Below is a diagram showing the manufacture of a cake made as a one-off prototype. Copy the diagram and rewrite the text to show how the cake would be made if it were being mass-produced.

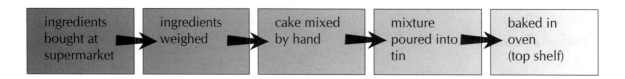

| ingredients bought at supermarket | → | ingredients weighed | → | cake mixed by hand | → | mixture poured into tin | → | baked in oven (top shelf) |

Q2 What does "CAM" stand for?

Q3 Write down three advantages of using CAM.

Q4 Copy out the diagram, and write down how CAM could be used at each stage of the manufacture of a pizza.

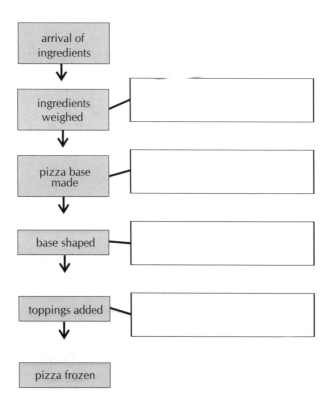

arrival of ingredients
↓
ingredients weighed
↓
pizza base made
↓
base shaped
↓
toppings added
↓
pizza frozen

Mass produced? Well, you shouldn't have eaten all those pies...

You'll need to make a prototype for your coursework. Then the best thing is probably to imagine how your product would be mass-produced. Alternatively you could buy a small factory somewhere and take on a number of staff (two or three hundred should be fine) to try it for real. But you won't get any extra marks.

Section Three — Food Processes

Food Contamination and Bacteria

Q1   Copy and complete these sentences using the words in the box below.

Food .... is a major concern for food manufacturers.
When you buy, ... , or store food, you also need to
make sure that you .... the risk of ....
You need to be sure that your food is .... to eat.

safe	prepare	contamination	safety	minimise

Q2   Briefly describe what bacteria are and list three places where they can be found.

Q3   Eating contaminated food can cause food poisoning. Briefly describe the typical symptoms
of food poisoning. Which groups of people are especially vulnerable to food poisoning?

Q4   Briefly explain what causes a food to have a high risk of
contamination by bacteria, and give four examples of such foods.

Q5   Copy and complete the equation below
which shows what bacteria need to multiply.

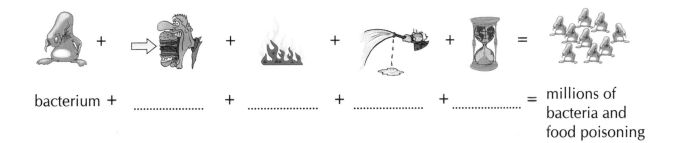

bacterium + ... + ... + ... + ... = millions of
bacteria and
food poisoning

Q6   A local restaurant has been accused of causing food poisoning.
Before it can reopen, they have to show that they have taken precautions
to prevent it happening again. Draw up a list of five rules which will
help them to promote good hygiene and avoid cross-contamination.

Preservation

Q1   Explain what we mean by preservation and give five methods of preserving foods.

Q2   Say which sentences are true and which are false.

a) Salt helps prevent bacteria growing by absorbing water from food.

b) Bacteria thrive on very large amounts of sugar.

c) Bacteria don't like acidic conditions, so adding vinegar
to food prevents them from multiplying.

Q3   Below are four methods of preserving food. Copy and complete
the following sentences using the words in the box below.

a) <u>Accelerated freeze-drying</u> — .... and flavour are preserved by ....
and drying the food very quickly in a ....

b) <u>Irradiation</u> — micro-organisms are killed by bombarding the food with
ionising ....

c) <u>Canning</u> — food is placed in the can, along with some additional ....
The can is sealed and then .... to 115 °C.

d) <u>Pasteurisation</u> — food is heated to a high temperature to .... any bacteria
present. The .... is carefully designed to prevent any new bacteria
.... the product.

freezing	radiation	contaminating	vacuum
liquid	heated	colour	destroy	packaging

Q4   Explain what "MAP" stands for and how it works.

HACCP

Q1   Food manufacturers are legally required to make sure that the food we eat is safe. When a new food is designed an HACCP system must be put in place. What does HACCP stand for?

Q2   Copy and complete this paragraph using the words in the box below.

HACCP is a .... designed to make sure that products are produced

.... and are of a high .... It's important to prevent ....

products being made which may pose a .... to consumers.

| quality | system | faulty | safely | risk |

Q3   Write out a brief definition of each of the terms below.

a)   hazard

b)   risk (in the context of hazards)

c)   risk assessment

Q4   There are three main types of hazard. Copy and complete the table below, giving a brief description of each.

Biological	
Chemical	
Physical	

Q5   A food manufacturer has been receiving complaints about their food. For each of the complaints below, suggest what procedures or checks the company could carry out to ensure it doesn't happen again.

a) A fly in a packet of cornflakes.

b) A screw in the middle of a loaf of bread.

c) An earring in a tin of soup.

d) Cigarette ends in a scone.

What's worse than finding a maggot in your cake?*

Don't let the complicated abbreviations fox you. HACCP and risk management are almost entirely about common sense. You see a problem, you think about it a bit and then you think up a way to minimise the risks.

*Finding a plaster with a scab still attached to it. Worse than half a maggot any day.

Setting Up Simple HACCP

Q1   HACCP needs to be set up step by step. Put the following
       sentences into the right order, to show how HACCP should be set up.

   a) Rewrite your steps as a simple flow chart.

   b) Write down some simple steps showing roughly how you plan to make your product.

   c) Then consider the potential hazards each step might involve.

   d) Think about the process of production from 'field to table'.

Q2   Most food comes into contact with humans at some point during its manufacture.
       Give three examples of how workers can cause a hazard in food production.

Q3   Below is a table showing the different stages of food production.
       For each stage, write down a hazard that could occur and the action that
       could be taken to stop it happening. The first one has been done for you.

	Hazard	Action
Purchase	Poor quality ingredients, contaminated with bacteria	Refuse to accept foods. Buy food from a good supplier
Storage		
Cooking		
Cooling		
Reheating		

Q4   Draw up an HACCP table like the one in Q3 for the making of
       a pizza. Your table should cover five stages: buying ingredients,
       making pizza dough, adding toppings, cooking and cooling.

Domestic Equipment

Q1   Say which sentences are true and which are false.

a) Electrical equipment speeds up the production of food.

b) Electrical equipment doesn't help to improve quality.

c) Using electrical equipment can help cut manufacturing costs.

d) Using electrical equipment produces less washing.

Q2   The table below shows some electrical equipment that you could use in project work. Copy the table and write an advantage and disadvantage of using each piece of equipment in your project.

Microwave	Advantage	
	Disadvantage	
Electric hand whisk	Advantage	
	Disadvantage	
Food processor	Advantage	
	Disadvantage	
Bread-maker	Advantage	
	Disadvantage	

Q3   Safety and hygiene are vital when using equipment.
Copy and complete the sentences below using the words in the box.

a)   It is important to wear .... clothing when using ....

b)   All equipment should be .... thoroughly and the users should have .... hands at all times.

c)   All equipment should be cleaned after use to prevent ....

d)   The equipment should have .... features, and all workers should be .... in how to use them.

| equipment | protective | clean | washed |
| cross-contamination | | trained | safety |

Q4   Write down what electrical equipment you could use to make each of the dishes below.

a) chocolate cake   b) vegetable soup   c) bread rolls

Industrial Equipment

Q1   Copy and complete the sentences below using the words in the box.

To make quality products with a high level of .... , it is essential
to weigh ingredients accurately. .... scales are more accurate
than .... scales, but not as good as computerised scales.

consistency	digital	balance

Q2   Computerised scales are the best ones to
use in industry. Give three reasons why.

Q3   Depositors are used to fill pastry cases, etc. Give three ways in which the
filling can be varied, and say why this is an advantage to the manufacturer.

Q4   The table below shows the four main types of industrial oven.
Copy and complete the table, writing a description of each type of oven.

Name of Oven	Description
Tunnel oven	
Convection oven	
Travel oven	
Deck oven	

Q5   Say which statements are true and which are false.

a) Mandolins are used to slice and cut foods into random shapes.

b) Centrifuges spin mixtures very fast, separating
liquid from the solid parts.

c) Vats are small containers used for storing portions of food.

d) Hoppers are huge holding containers which can weigh out the
correct amounts of ingredients.

I like to call a spade a piece of industrial gardening equipment...

There's other equipment as well, you know. Floor-standing mixers are like giant food processors — they can
mix massive quantities of ingredients evenly and consistently. Then there are silos, which are basically giant
containers. And of course, you shouldn't go into your exam without knowing all about oompa-loompas.

Section Three — Food Processes

Target Groups

Q1 When developing a new food product, you should have a target group in mind. Describe what a target group is.

Q2 At which stage of the design process should you decide who your target group is?

Q3 McWumpy are going to develop a new snack product. They're not sure of the best way to begin the process. Copy out the stages of development below in the correct order.

Make some snack foods and get people to try them out.

Produce a questionnaire to find out people's preferences and views on snack products.

Decide who your target group is going to be.

Identify groups of people with specific needs for whom you could develop your new product.

Q4 Different target groups may have specific nutritional needs. Copy and complete the following sentences about nutritional needs, choosing the correct words from the brackets.

a) (Toddlers / Elderly people) need nutrients such as calcium and protein for growth and development.

b) Women who are (inactive / pregnant) need extra protein, calcium and iron.

c) Diabetics need to follow a healthy diet and to cut down on (fats and oils / carbohydrates and sugars).

d) Sporty, active people should have plenty of foods that provide (vitamins / energy).

e) People who are overweight or who have a sedentary lifestyle should eat (low-fat / special diet) foods.

f) The elderly usually lead sedentary lifestyles and so don't need as much (fat and carbohydrates / calcium and vitamins) as young people.

g) (Breast-feeding women / Vegetarians) may need extra vitamin B12.

Q5 McWumpy may choose their target group by identifying 'personal preferences' rather than dietary requirements. Name three personal preferences that foods may be targeted towards.

Other Factors Affecting People's Choices

Q1   Which of the following describes what organic food is?

   a) Foods that are cooked by well-organised people.

   b) Foods that contain organisms from other animals or plants.

   c) Foods that are produced without the use of chemical fertilizers or insecticides.

Q2   List three ways in which takeaway foods can have a bad effect on the environment.

Q3   Give two ways in which manufacturers could be more
      environmentally friendly in their production of packaging.

We all say GM
foods are ace.

Q4   Copy and complete the following sentences, choosing
      the right word to finish each one off correctly.

   a) Thickeners or gelling agents are used to increase thickness or to produce a
      gel in (sauces / cakes).

   b) Preservatives are used to protect the food from the growth of microbes and
      so increase (colour / shelf-life).

   c) Emulsifiers help to form an emulsion between oil and water and so prevent
      separation during storage. This makes them more (stable / unstable).

   d) Colourings are used to improve the appearance of many foods.
      They are added to foods that have lost colour during (cooking / storage).

   e) To improve the nutritional value of breakfast cereals, most have had
      vitamins and minerals (added / removed).

   f) Artificial sweeteners are used in many low-calorie desserts and drinks in
      place of (flavours / sugar).

Q5   In recent years there has been an increase in the use of genetically modified
      (GM) foods. Many people have been concerned and have campaigned to have
      GM foods banned. Give two advantages and two disadvantages of GM foods.

Standard Food Components

Q1   Mandy has decided to make a special meal for her boyfriend, for their two-week anniversary. She has decided to use some standard food components in the meal. What is meant by the phrase 'standard food components'?

Q2   Mandy has decided to make pizza, coleslaw and a special meringue pudding. Which of the following bought ingredients are standard food components?

For the pizza:

block of cheddar cheese

tomato purée

pizza base

ready chopped vegetables

pizza topping sauce

grated mozzarella cheese

pepperoni sausage

sliced meat

flour

yeast

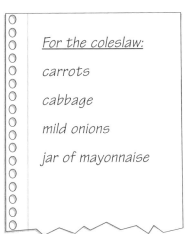

For the coleslaw:

carrots

cabbage

mild onions

jar of mayonnaise

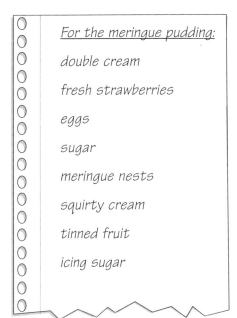

For the meringue pudding:

double cream

fresh strawberries

eggs

sugar

meringue nests

squirty cream

tinned fruit

icing sugar

Q3   Food manufacturers use many standard food components which they buy in. There are many advantages to using standard food components. Write a sentence to answer each of the following questions.

a) How can using standard food components save a company money?

b) How is it possible to save time by using standard food components?

c) Quality of food can be guaranteed when using standard food components. Why?

d) Why is the production of foods more hygienic when standard food components are used?

e) What effect does using standard food components have on the need for machinery?

Onions aren't standard — but there's not shallot we can do...

The stuff on this page is pretty straightforward really. As long as you know what standard food components are, you should be okay. Make sure you managed to explain everything in Question 3 too — that's the kind of stuff you'll be expected to know. Good. Now go and have an onion.

Labelling

Q1 Netti is a new supermarket chain that produces many 'own label' foods. The design staff have to design labels for all the 'own label' food products on sale. Name the four laws that the design team should refer to in making sure that they don't break any laws when labelling foods.

Q2 Choose words from the box below to complete the following sentences about food labelling.

a) The .... indicates when the product should be used by to minimise the risk of
   ....

b) The .... instructions give guidance on what you should do with the product when you get it home from the shops. This can prolong the .... of the product.

c) All ingredients should be listed in .... order of weight. You can also sometimes find out the actual .... of a particular ingredient in a product.

d) All labels must, by law, show the .... and .... of the manufacturer.

e) The labelling should show instructions for .... and .... the product.

f) All food products must have the .... of the .... on the label and must also tell you what the product is. Labelling must not make any false claims about what the food is.

g) Recently a law was passed that stated that manufacturers must say on the label if a product contains .... ingredients.

use-by date	weight	storage
preparation	name	shelf-life	name
storage	address	product	food poisoning
genetically modified	descending	

Labelling and Packaging

Q1 The food technologists at Netti have developed a new range of special 'low-fat' foods.

    a) Why must the nutritional information, by law, be shown on the label in this case?

    b) List the nutritional information usually found on a food label.

    c) Why do you think that nutritional information is usually listed 'per 100 g'?

    d) How could the fact that the nutritional information is listed 'per 100 g' help a customer who was trying to lose weight?

Q2 What is this, and why is it used on foods?

Q3 What does this symbol represent?

Q4 Why do some foods have symbols on to represent that they are suitable for a special diet?

Q5 Give one advantage and one disadvantage of each of the following packaging materials.

a) glass

b) plastic

c) aluminium

d) paper and cardboard

Q6 MAP is a technique used to help preserve foods.

    a) What do the initials MAP stand for?

    b) Explain how MAP is used to extend the shelf-life of fresh foods.

    c) What happens to a food's shelf-life once its packet has been opened?

Q7 Briefly explain how vacuum packaging works.

Evaluation and Development

Q1   If you're going to develop a really good food product you need to follow the design process in the correct order. Sort out the following stages into the correct order.

> development
> initial ideas
> manufacturing specification
> research
> final evaluation

Q2   Deciding on your target group needs to be done early on in the development stage. Different types of products are going to appeal to different groups of people. Say which groups of people you think the following products might appeal to.

a)   high-energy fruit drink

b)   low-fat cream cakes

c)   Hagrid's 'orrible fruit bars

d)   gluten-free biscuits

e)   vegetable lasagne

Q3   What is brainstorming, and how can it help in the development of your product?

Q4   Early in the development of a food product you'll need to find out how to make it better than its rivals — so that it sells well. List four things that you will have to find out in order to do this.

Darwin's theory of evaluation — only the best cakes are reproduced...

Make sure you record all stages of your development process. Examiners are dead keen on this — more so even than research, because it's all <u>your</u> work rather than stuff you found on the net.

More Development

Q1 Once you've got the initial ideas under way you'll need to make a
few prototypes. What can you learn from making a prototype?

Q2 Developing food products need to be tested after
each new stage of development. List four aspects that
will need testing each time, whatever the product.

Testing Procedure:
1. Is it food?
2. Is it food?
3. Is it food?
4. Is it food?

Q3 Testing out prototypes should help you come up with even more ideas and
ways that you can develop your initial ideas. Copy the chart below and give
some suggestions as to how each product could be adjusted and developed.

Product Fault	Improvements
Lemon cheesecake that doesn't taste of lemon	
Bread rolls that lack flavour	
Spaghetti sauce that lacks tomato flavour	
Chilli made with beef for vegetarians	

Q4 One of the secrets of good development work is to make sure you record absolutely
everything that you do. If you were going to make a prototype of spaghetti bolognese
made with soya mince instead of beef, what sorts of things would you record?

And Yet More Development

Q1 Development is all about finding ways to change and improve your ideas. Copy out the table below and then fill in suggestions of how you can make the changes required.

Changing the colour of food products without resorting to artificial food dyes	
Thickening sauces and other cooked dishes	
Setting cold desserts	
Sweetening food without adding more refined sugar	
Stopping fruit going brown (oxidising)	
Creating healthier options	
Improving savoury food that seems to be lacking flavour	

Q2 This question is not as silly as it might sound.
Why do manufacturers bother to develop new food products?

Q3 Different target groups have different needs, and you'll have to think about these in your product development. Write down one special requirement that each of the following groups of people might need in a food product.

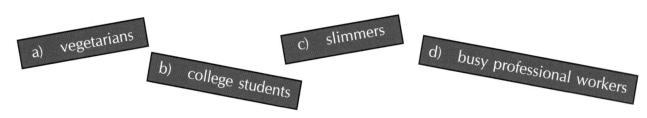

a) vegetarians

b) college students

c) slimmers

d) busy professional workers

Q4 In a taste-test of a prototype of vegetable soup, you have had the following feedback from your tasters. How could you start to improve this soup?

"not much flavour"

"I didn't like the lumps of vegetable floating in it"

"I would like some protein in this soup but I'm also a vegetarian"

Data Collection and Analysis

Q1   In what ways can ICT help you collect information that
will be useful in the development of your product?

Q2   Copy and complete the passage below, using words from the box.

To develop a new product you need as much .... as possible

about existing .... already on the market. You will need to know

the .... of them as well as their .... You will also need to know

the .... and .... of your target group.

information	dislikes	cost
likes	products	ingredients

Q3   Your company is producing a new shepherd's pie, aimed at university students.
You've found out that the students are particularly concerned about the cost of the product,
whether it's healthy and whether it's environmentally friendly. Suggest ways that you could
change the recipe below to fit in with their concerns, and give reasons for your changes.

Shepherd's Pie

250 g minced beef

1 onion

500 g potatoes

1 tin of tomatoes

50 g butter

1 stock cube

pinch of mixed herbs

*packaged in plastic cook/chill tray,
wrapped in clear plastic and
packaged in cardboard box*

Q4   Finding out the cost of rival products by wandering round shops and writing down prices can
be time-consuming — and you can get funny looks from shop assistants. However, there are
quicker ways to compare prices from several different supermarkets. How could you do it?

Get the information, then decide what changes to make...

Exams almost always get you to suggest how to change a recipe for different groups of consumers.
Make sure you learn about the main dietary requirements of different groups of people, e.g. low-fat
products for slimmers, soya milk for vegans, food without nuts for people with nut allergies...

Questionnaires

Q1 You've carried out a questionnaire about what students at your school eat in the canteen. Look at the results on the right. What do they tell you, and how would you deal with these differing results?

Children mainly eat:
salad sandwiches,
orange juice,
fruit

Canteen's biggest sellers:
chips and gravy,
canned fizzy drinks,
chocolate bars

Q2 Doris and Fred both carry out a questionnaire about the same sorts of things. In the chart below are a few of the questions that they asked. Fred gets a much better selection of data to work with than Doris, yet their questions are trying to find out the same information. Explain why you think this is.

Doris's Questions	Fred's Questions
How old are you?	Tick which age group you are: 10-20, 20-30, 30-40, 40-50, 50-60 or over 60.
Do you do lots of exercise?	How many times a week do you take part in exercise: none / one / two / over two times a week?
Do you eat healthy food?	Tick any of the following foods that you eat on a regular basis: low-fat spread / olive oil / wholemeal bread / fresh fruit / fresh vegetables

Q3 List the three basic <u>types</u> of question you can use in a questionnaire, and give an example of each.

Q4 Targeting where you hand out questionnaires can save time and get much more accurate information. Write down where you think the best place would be to hand out questionnaires if you wanted to collect data about each of the following:

views about healthy eating for toddlers

views about low-calorie products

opinions about organic ready-made meals

opinions about school meals

Presenting and Analysing Results

Q1 There are several different types of charts and some are better at illustrating information than others. Say which sort of chart would be the best for each of the following collections of data.

a) The most popular flavours of ice cream for 15-year-olds.

b) The monthly consumption of ice cream by 15-year-olds for a year.

c) How many times a week 15-year-olds ate ice cream during August.

Q2 Once you have collected your data and presented it in the form of a chart, you must analyse and draw conclusions from it. What conclusions could you draw from the chart below?

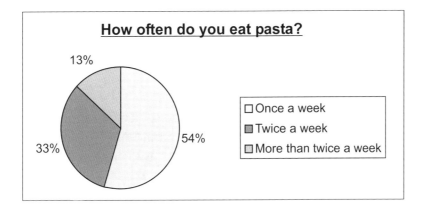

How often do you eat pasta?

13%
33%
54%

☐ Once a week
■ Twice a week
☐ More than twice a week

Q3 Hopefully you have got this drilled into you by now, but just for old times' sake, write out this sentence using the correct word from the choices.

Graphs and charts are USELESS if they're not (pink / labelled / singing / making toast).

Q4 The chart below shows the data from Q2. What information is missing?

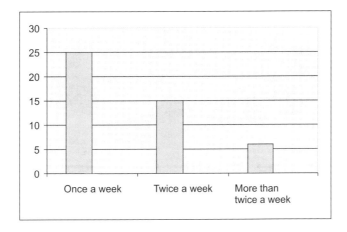

Once a week   Twice a week   More than twice a week

Product Analysis

Q1   What is disassembly and what sorts of factors would you be looking at if you were going to disassemble a bacon, lettuce and tomato sandwich?

Q2   Some responses from disassembling a product are of more help to you than others. Write down the responses that you think would not be very helpful, and say why.

   a)   I didn't like the smell.

   b)   There was too much chocolate icing.

   c)   Over 50% of the total weight of the cake came from the chocolate icing.

   d)   The packaging lacked colour and did not have a photograph on it.

   e)   The packaging was dull.

Q3   You couldn't disassemble a sponge cake other than by separating the icing and filling from the cake, as the ingredients are impossible to separate once it's been cooked. However you could look at some other points. Suggest two such points.

Q4   It's useful to vary the words you use to describe foods — e.g. the word 'nice' is often overused and is not very descriptive. Give two possible alternatives for the word 'nice' in each of the following:

   a)   It smells nice

   b)   It looks nice

   c)   It tastes nice

Q5   When you're analysing your product you will need to compare costs. If you were just going on cost alone, which one of the following would be the best value?

Product A at £1.50 for 100 g

Product B at £3.20 for 200 g

Product C at £3.90 for 300 g

Too much chocolate icing? — surely not possible...

Remember — good value doesn't always mean the cheapest. For example, a scrummy chocolate pie that costs £6 is probably better value than one costing £5 that makes you sick.

Packaging Analysis

Q1   When carrying out a product analysis you will need to look hard at the packaging, especially the ingredients list. As well as telling you what ingredients are in the food product, what else does the list tell you?

Q2   The font that the designer has used on the packaging can give you a hint as to the target group the product is aimed at. Take a look at the styles below and suggest a target group that they may be being aimed at.

a)   **Cheese and Tomato Pizza**

b)   *Cheese and Tomato Pizza*

c)   **Cheese and Tomato Pizza**

Q3   Products often form part of a range of products. The choice of the name can also influence the people likely to buy it. Copy and complete the table below to show who you think the ranges might be aimed at.

The Green Café	
Captain Meganosh	
Bartolli's Bistro	
Lean and Mean	
Classic Cuisine	

Sensory Analysis

Q1   Sensory testing needs you to use all your senses. Copy and complete the table below,
giving an example of how you might use each sense in the sensory testing of a food product.

Sense	Example of Use

Q2   If you were doing a sensory analysis on the following food products,
what order of senses would you test them in and why?

Chicken in White Wine and Cream Sauce	Chicken Vindaloo
Sweet and Sour Chicken	Chicken Tikka Masala

Q3   Star diagrams are an excellent way of recording sensory analysis because
they allow you to see the characteristics of a food at a glance. Draw a star
diagram with the characteristics you might test for each of the dishes below.

crunchy oat biscuits

chilli con carne

lemon mousse

*Star diagrams are sometimes called
star profiles or radar graphs — it just
depends which book you read.*

Q4   If sensory testing is to be useful it must be done under carefully controlled conditions.
List four things that you could do to make sure that your sensory testing is fair and accurate.

Fe fi fo fum — I smell the whiff of a poppadum...

Avoid the temptation to let everyone dig in with a spoon as soon as you've finished cooking.
They might be tasting your product, but it's not 'sensory testing' unless it's properly controlled.

Section Five — Design and Development

Control Systems and Feedback

Q1 All systems can be broken down into three parts.
Fill in the names of the parts in the boxes below.

1. ➡ **2.** ➡ **3.**

Q2 Copy the table below, write in the parts of a system (your answers to Q1),
then complete the table for a particular system using words from the box.

Part of System:	1.	2.	3.
Examples:			

flour   margarine   baking powder   mixing   measuring   weighing   scones   sugar
milk   shaping   cooking   cooling   rolling pin   cutters   food processor

Q3 A good system will use feedback so that a high quality product can be guaranteed.
Here is part of a simple system for shaping and filling flan cases:

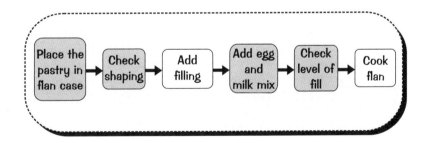

Place the pastry in flan case ➡ Check shaping ➡ Add filling ➡ Add egg and milk mix ➡ Check level of fill ➡ Cook flan

Say where you think the best points for feedback are and explain
how the product might be returned to the previous stage.

Q4 Write a sentence to explain how
ICT can help improve feedback.

*Get as many references to computers into your
work as possible — the examiners love them.
Systems are the perfect opportunity to do it.*

Quality Control and Assurance

Q1 Write a couple of sentences explaining the difference between quality control and quality assurance.

Q2 Unfortunately the following products have managed to reach the supermarket shelves. For each product suggest two checks that have failed in the factory.

a) Cherry biscuits which have no cherries in them.

b) Burnt crust on a loaf of bread.

c) Not enough cheese on a cheese and tomato pizza.

d) A small piece of metal in a chocolate biscuit.

Q3 A factory produces thousands of identical loaves of bread a day. Make a list of five parts of the bread-making process that will need to be constant in order for this to happen.

1.
2.
3.
4.
5.

Q4 How does HACCP help to control quality?

Q5 A manufacturer wants to be sure that the chocolate muffins they are manufacturing are all the same colour. Suggest three things that they must ensure are quality checked on the production line.

This is muffin control.
You are 'Go' for muffin wrapping.